1971

This book may be kept

FOURTEEN DAYS

A fine will be charged for each day the book is kept overtime.

DE 2 7			
OCT 24 '74			
NOV 21 '74			
DEC 12 '74			
MAY 5 '75			
OCT 7 1976			
GAYLORD 142			PRINTED IN U.S.A.

Finding
A Poem

Finding
A Poem

by Eve Merriam

illustrated by
Seymour Chwast

ATHENEUM *1970* NEW YORK

Contents

Finding
A Poem

The Wholly Family

Baby's got a plastic bottle,
plastic pacifier to chew;
plastic pillows on the sofa,
plastic curtains frame the view;
plastic curlers do up Mama,
Mama's hairdo plastic, too.

Junior plays with plastic modules,
Sister pins on plastic bows;
plastic wallet made for Papa,
plastic credit cards in rows;
plastic ivy in the planter
greener than the real thing grows.

Plastic pumpkin for Thanksgiving,
plastic beach ball by the sea;
plastic snow at Christmastime,
plastic manger, star and tree;
plastic used so totally
keeps us germproof and dirt-free.

      Praise of plastic thus we sing,
      plastic over everything
      keeps us cool and safe and dry:
      it may not pain us much to die.

Calendar

Someday wooed a peacock,
Monday thought of molt;
Someday flung the window,
Tuesday drew the bolt.

Wednesday dried the dishes,
Someday dribbled juice;
Thursday counted dollar bills,
Someday's coins cut loose.

Friday wore a raincoat,
Someday splashed the boss;
Saturday looked to and fro,
Someday leaped across.

Ah oneday come moonday
come chooseday   come whensday
my hersday   my freeday
my satyrday SUN!

Sandwriting

Smooth the edges of jagged glass
and let time pass.

Old people beached up on the shore
to and fro   to and fro
rocking on a dry sea
of memory.

A night on the mountain,
a day in the valley,
the years and the years
come and go,
come and
go.

Interview

What would you like to be?

A waterfall   a flying fish   a tree

Seriously
what will you do
when you're through school?

Float leap dig ramble poke run

Don't be foolish,
don't you know you have to earn a living?

Oh you mean a dying
well get a job I guess
the same as you
and cover up the sun

Umbilical

You can take away my my mother,
you can take away my sister,
but don't take away
my little transistor.

I can do without sunshine,
I can do without Spring,
but I can't do without
my ear to that thing.

I can live without water,
in a hole in the ground,
but I can't live without
that sound that sound that sound that sOWnd.

Some Little Poems Without
   the Word
      Love

   1.

Where else
would I
take
my
troubles?

   2.

In French
joie
is a rhyme for
toi.

   3.

When it rains,
I miss you
and
when
the rain stops,
then
too.

   4.

Every morning when I awaken,
I open the cage of my mouth
and your name
flies forth.

Neuteronomy

The elevator stops at every floor
and nobody opens and closes the door,
and nobody talks to his neighbor anymore
where the neuter computer goes *tick,*
where the neuter computer goes *click.*

You call the operator on the telephone
and say Help! I'm in trouble and I'm here all alone!
and all you get back is a phoney dial tone
where the neuter computer goes *clank,*
where the neuter computer goes *blank.*

There's no more teacher to be nice or mean
when you learn your lessons from a teaching machine
and plug in your prayers to the preaching machine
where the neuter computer goes *bless,*
where the neuter computer noes *yes.*

From when you are born until you are old
the facts of your life are all controlled,
put your dreams on a punch card—don't staple or fold
where the neuter computer prints *file,*
where the neuter computer prints *smile.*

There's no one to love and no one to hate,
and no more misfortune or chance or fate
in this automated obligated zero perfect state
where the neuter computer goes *think*,
where the neuter computer goes *blink*
  blink think blink think blink blink blink
    blinkthink
    thinkblink
    blink
     think
      blink

Alarm Clock

in the deep sleep forest
there were ferns
there were feathers
there was fur
and a soft ripe peach
on a branch within my

r-r-r-r-r-r-r-r-r-r-r-r-r-r-r-r-r-r-r-r-r-r-r-r-r-r-r-r-r-r-r-r

Witness

In a time like this time,
in a town like this town,
an angel flew on down.
Angel, angel on the way!
Angel coming here today
with a flaming sword and a golden pen,
come to bring the word to the world of men.
Angel, angel, welcome in!

FIRST CITIZEN: I saw some kind of shadow pass across the door,
but I don't open up the bolt anymore.
This neighborhood's not what it used to be,
and I don't take any chances, no not me.
My charity donations go by mail,
and I don't need a notice for any special sale.
Don't want free samples today or any day,
they're never really free, you always have to pay.
No. I said no. I said GO AWAY.

Angel, angel circling round,
where is sanctuary found?

SECOND CITIZEN: I heard a funny kind of flapping noise,
but I thought it was the kids with their bang-bang
toys.
And there's all this wrecking and blasting around,
digging up and drilling holes in the ground.
Still, I heard some funny kind of crying sighing
sound . . .
But there's so much traffic and horns that blow,

16

cars and jets and buses and cabs on the go;
still, I heard that funny kind of whimper and so—
I turned up the volume on my radio.

Angel, angel circling low,
angel, angel—no, oh no!

THIRD CITIZEN: It happened right there in front of me,
came close to the accident as anyone could be;
but it's a free country and I don't have to say,
play it safe and smart and walk on away.
I don't want to have to testify in court,
can't get involved, life's too short.
Besides, I've got a wife and two kids to support.
Feel bad about it, but I can always pray,
and suppose I'd had to be somewhere else today?

In a time like this time,
in a town like this town

an angel

      flew

          on

    down.

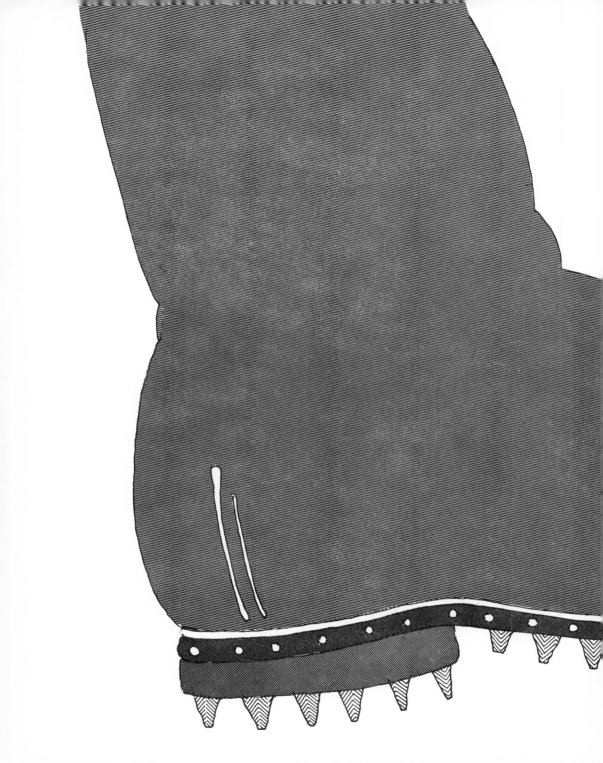

The Measure of Man

It has been estimated that
the most medium living thing
standing
exactly halfway in between
the smallest crawling gnat
and the tallest spouting
giant blue whale
is
man.

Of course on a different scale
say
ability to create
or greater yet
annihilate
there's
nothing
halfway
about him.

Fantasia

I dream
of
giving birth
to
a child
who will ask
"Mother,
what was war?"

Cult

A many-colored dome holds up the sky.
Fountains abound, music's a presence unseen.
The aisles are wide. Worshippers walk between,
lifting their eyes to the sermon mounted high:
Founder's Day bargains, discount on all you buy.

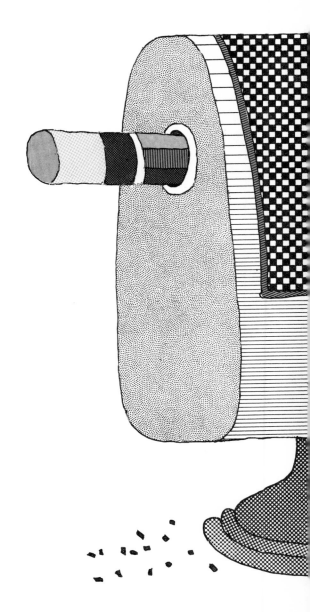

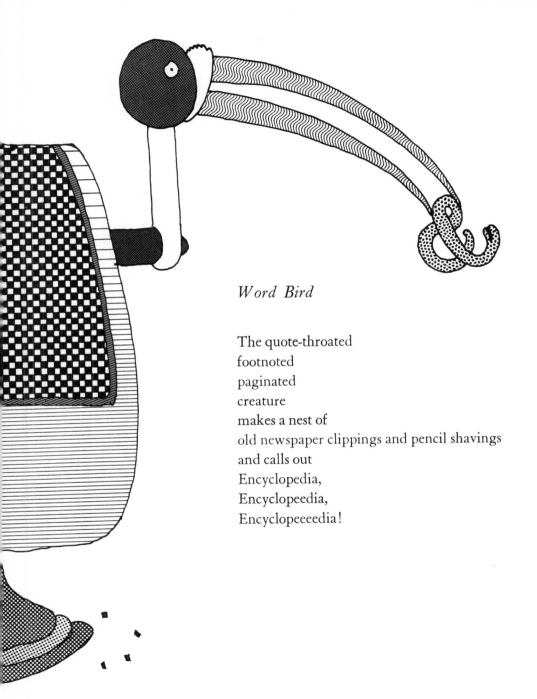

Word Bird

The quote-throated
footnoted
paginated
creature
makes a nest of
old newspaper clippings and pencil shavings
and calls out
Encyclopedia,
Encyclopeedia,
Encyclopeeeedia!

23

Markings: The Period

Left.   Right.
Left.   Right.
Absolute black.
Positive white.

Those in the know
march straight in a row.
Never a moment's hesitancy.
No raggedy baggy-kneed stragglers like me
who bumble along half-right and
not quite . . .

Markings: The Question

?

A scythe
flailing away
at the wandering field
of why.

Who can cut down
the mysterious grain
that rises high again
with secrets unrevealed?

Markings: The Exclamation

!

The racing flag whips out:
no second place,
no third-in-show.
Winner take all.
GO!

!

Markings: The Comma

,

A short pause,
like waiting for the traffic light to change,
and looking at the person next to you
until the green comes on
and you move along
and he turns into a stranger once again,
the same as you.

Markings: The Semicolon

;

Diver on the board
lunges toward the edge;
hedges;
takes a deep breath;
hesitates;

    plunges.

Showers, Clearing Later in the Day

```
 !! !! !!   ! !   !
!!!!!!!! !!!! !! !!!
!!!!!!!!!!!!!!!!!!!!!!!!!!!
!!!!!!!!!!!!!!!!!!!!!!!!!!
!!!!!!!!!!!!!!!!!!!!!!!!!!!!!!!        !!!!!
     !!!!!!!! !!!!!!!!!!!
    **!!!!!!!!!!!
          !!  ! !!
         * ! * !

              ..   * ! ! ...
         *...


                  .



    *
    .

          .
```

Llude Sig Kachoo

Wed flowers bloob
with sweet perfube
or sdowflakes fall
upod the growd
as dature bakes
its yearly rowd:
subber,
autub,
widder,
sprig;
the cobbod code
its gerbs
doth brig.

Ping-Pong

Chitchat
wigwag
rickrack
zigzag

knickknack
gewgaw
riffraff
seesaw

crisscross
flip-flop
ding-dong
tiptop

singsong
mishmash
King Kong
       bong.

A Number of Words

wanton

to-do

threne

forfend

fiveling

sixain

sevenbark

aitchbone

nighness

tenet

Rumor

It's an old adage

Pass on the message

Peas Porridge hot

Free storage for pots

What sort of party

Horrible orgy

Urbanity

Everybody
knows
how an orange
grows
on a tree
because
you can see
the frozen-juice commercials
on teevee.

Miss Hepzibah

Miss Hepzibah has a mania
for stuffing unsorted miscellania
into her net reticule:

a tortoise-shell back-scratcher for her cat,
a button hook for a gray suede spat,
a patent leather feather to trim a hat,
a horsehair locket, a butterfly tray, a whalebone stay,
an elephant tusk, a tippet of muskrat, a tin of sassafras tea,
jelly of rose hips, lavender smelling salts, extract of lilac
and an excerpt of purple prose
to go with her bifocal glasses, molasses in jugs,
a moosehead umbrella stand,
witch hazel elixir, licorice whips, a taffeta headache band,
rhubarb and soda, oil of macassar, a scalloped lace doily,
a fencing foil, a motoring veil, a camisole, a farthingale,
a metronome, a wooden egg darner, a butter paddle, saddle soap,
a mortar and pestle, a candlestick snuffer, a chamois buffer,
a needlepoint footstool, a flannel chest liner, a little nightcap,
and underneath all
a lunatic-fringèd shawl.

A Round

Spaghetti,
spaghetti,
heaped in a mound;

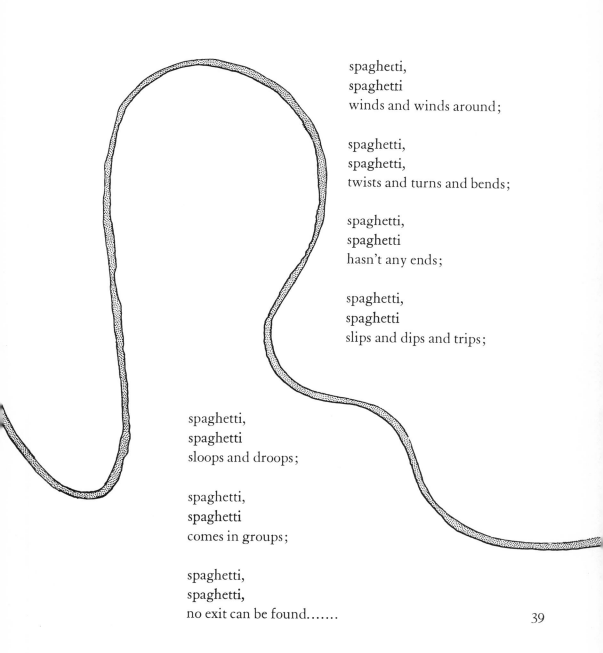

spaghetti,
spaghetti
winds and winds around;

spaghetti,
spaghetti,
twists and turns and bends;

spaghetti,
spaghetti
hasn't any ends;

spaghetti,
spaghetti
slips and dips and trips;

spaghetti,
spaghetti
sloops and droops;

spaghetti,
spaghetti
comes in groups;

spaghetti,
spaghetti,
no exit can be found.......

39

Basic for Irresponsibility

IT is a useful word.
IT can do many things.

IT cannot shine,
the sun does that.
But IT can rain,
and IT can snow.

IT can look like trouble ahead.
IT can look like the end of non-violence.
IT can even look like another war.
I would not want IT to happen,
and you would not want IT to happen,
but we have nothing to do with IT.

IT is not my fault
any more than IT is your fault.
IT is nobody's fault.
IT is just the way things are.

That is the way IT goes.

IT goes by itself.
We do not have to approve of IT.
We do not have to do anything at all about IT.
That is the best way for IT to grow.

Basic for Further Irresponsibility

THEY is another useful word.
You can use THEY to scare people
like on Hallowe'en.

Boo.
THEY say there's going to be a long hot summer starting early
and lasting all year round.
Boo, boo.
THEY say some people just don't understand law and order.
Boo, boo, boo.
THEY say some people have to have law and order pounded into
    them.
That's what THEY say.

I don't say so,
and you don't,
but that's what THEY say.

It's easy to play THEY.
You don't need numbers or paper or a pencil
or a ball or a net or a stand or any kind of base for support.
THEY just make it all up,
and we go along.

Basic for Better Living

Enjoy yourself.
Live better.
Enjoy yourself and live better
with a clean fresh-tasting cigarette.

Enjoy yourself and live better
with a clean fresh-tasting cigarette with a filter
to filter out the harmful nicotine and tar.

Enjoy yourself and live better
with a clean fresh-tasting cigarette with
a filter to filter out the harmful nicotine and tar and with
menthol to take away that cotton filter taste.

Enjoy yourself with the cool sweet minty flavor
and then
really enjoy yourself
and live better than ever
with a cigarette without a fuzzing filter
and without harsh menthol that kills the filter waste that takes away
the rich tobacco taste
of the
cig-
ugh-
rette.   43

The Happy Cynic to His Love

As rain to holiday,
burn to sun,
as chilling damp to grass;

as traffic and stall,
train and late,
go and do not pass;

as prices and rise,
pollute and skies,
as no waiting now and wait;

as mugger to purse,
bad and worse,
so, dearest one,
I yearn to be your mate.

Ways of Winding a Watch

1.

a little forward   a little back
a little back   a little bored don't be
a little forward   you've got to keep going
a little back   back a little for
a little forward   ward a lit a back a for
                  a bac   kthere!

2.

long forward motions
sloop sloop like a wild ice-skater
hardly glancing back to shore at all

3.

slow
easy
before it really needs it
smug oh teacher's pet   oh mama's darling
oh put your scarf and gloves on

4.

backwards first
may get there anywayz

5.

shake it   *Oh you-----!*

6.

shake it tenderly   *oh, you....*

45

7.

hit it smartly
like a butter knife clopping the top of a soft-boiled egg
in its shell cup

8.

smash it

9.

keep it at the same time always   a remembrance of this moment

The Seasons on Our Block

Mrs. Mayer, Mrs. Mayer,
growing leaner, sadder, grayer.

Her husband dead, her children grown,
tends the cleaning store alone.

Your coat, she frowns, had a very bad spot,
and Hot, she frowns in summer, Hot.

Fall, she sighs, it's time for school,
already it feels a little too cool.

Winter, she huddles as dark winds blow,
the winter's never going to go.

But under the sky of springtime blue
Mrs. Mayer smiles at you.

Dream Voyage to the Center
of the Subway

1.

One day
the billboards all implore
"Buy Nothing"

2.

In the broken vending machine
push the plunger
and pop out
a flower
sprung dewborn
fresh every hour

3.

Permanent graffiti:
    NATURE LOVES MAN
        MAN LOVES FELLOWMAN
           FELLOWMAN LOVES NATURE
    O HAPPY HOLY TRINITY

Finding a Poem

I.

Trail climbing
you have to watch your footing
tricky with fallen rocks and mosses that crumble
leafmold slippery
hold onto a bush
it springs back
scratching your face
your heart is pounding
your legs are ready to cave in
why do mountains have to be so steep
can't they put them in the plain

you can barely discern the ferns and laurel
amid the tangled brush
the evergreens *are* majestic but
sweating you've rubbed a blister
bugs to slap away
a dried-out stream bed
stony stony
until abruptly
light dazzling
you're in the clear
the air is the highest note ever sung
listen you can hear it echoing
all the way down
while here you kingly are
crowning the world
with this view that

is impossible to describe
a poem.

2.

Where there seems no way to go
go anyway
don't be put off by what you can't see
get up any which way
scramble on hands and knees
ditching your pride
slide along the bottom for a stretch
clutch at roots
and keep going on

once up there you can look back to
the pathway you have cleared
that will make it easier
next time you climb.

3.

Climbing often
not just for the music
but for the in between
the lights and darks of greenery
the patterns of touch

make a ritual
of going round the same trees
sitting on the same lichen benches

pausing for second breath at the same log
a tradition by now
and yet
you can never duplicate the climb
every time is the first anew.

Screen

Diving into the movie dark
we are champion swimmers
at home in lagoons
where the fish all
have heart-shaped mouths
and do not smell of fish.

When the lights go on,
we kick up to the surface
and have to be
pulled into nets
held by the sweating
hands of women and men.

The Dirty Word

swallow it raw

    awr

      rwa

        arw

          rwa

WAR

And Son

A family business, not many of them left.
Radiator covers, bookcases, shelving, desks, picture frames,
whatever you need, don't worry, we'll work it out.
The father takes measurements,
you'll see, we'll custom make it lady and cheaper than Macy's.
The quiet fat wife sits by the phone and nods,
while the carpenter son saws away in the back.

Yes, says the thin-faced father,
I'm a lucky man and I know it,
not many any more have a boy
willing to stick by the folks.
We go out on a job and if he drives the car,
you know it's crazy,
we can double park and never get a ticket,
but if he's not along with me—
a fifteen-dollar fine,
count your life on it every time.
I think it means a father and son belong together,
the family,
but it's hard nowadays,
I count my blessings, yes,
and only pray
the army doesn't take him.

What is there about the sight of a beat-up car, stripped, smashed and abandoned on city street or country road? To me it seems to epitomize the destruction of our natural landscape more than any other uglification. Soda bottles and beer cans, candy wrappers, plastic containers: all the messy sticky dangerous bits that foul the landscape are blightful but manageable. You can pick up the trash and remove it. Billboards can be zoned out of areas. But the cars keep coming on, new ones turning to used the instant they're sold. The scrapped car is a mechanical elephant, a Goliath of debris, too heavy and expensive to haul away; even the junkman won't take it for free junk.

In nature, leaves rot and become compost heap; all of human nature eventually turns to dust; the metal monsters, however, rust and remain.

Thinking about them one day, I wondered if they'd ever get to cover the earth as a new vegetation. Or else, I speculated, on Doomsday when everybody and everything else is gone, the cars will be all that is left.

A poem began as a first line came to me.

What will you find at the edge of the world?

I don't know why the expression came as *edge* instead of *end,* but it did, and through almost every stage of revision I retained it. Now, looking back, I can surmise that *edge* gives more of a visual picture than the abstracted concept *end,* and considering that I was writing about automobiles, *edge* suggests a road, but at the time there was no intellectualization involved. For whatever it was worth, the phrase came as a gift.

Scribbling the line on a note pad, I began to sketch a framework more consciously. I felt I wanted a rhyme, a formal pattern to enclose the thought. What would go with *world?* I put down as an initial phrase "a feather curled" and then the following:

```
#1            a cave
                   a cloud
                        dust
                           leaf
                              voice
          guitar
                     or an abandoned car?
                     bottle broken?
```

I put this rough sketch away and came back to it about a week later. *Guitar,* I could see was simply a rhyme for *car* and made no sense in the context. Nor did I care for *a feather curled;* it was strained, and also there just for the rhyme's sake, although the image of a single feather was something that might be kept—it seemed to connote the kind of finality I was searching for. Here is the second sketch.

```
#2       What will you find at the edge of the world?
           a polar icecap
                        a footprint,     a feather,
           a moon flag unfurled
                             a cave     wave
           a lunar guitar
                             a seagull feather curled
              a lunar scar     a spaceship spar
                                  hurled
```

59

signs of what people left to save
    light from a star
      or a broken bottle and a junked car?
    paper scraps   rusted
                      cans

As you can see, I was not yet working with the single-minded idea of cars as all that was left. Mainly my consciousness was fooling around with images and rhymes simultaneously, and like the old which-comes-first-the-chicken-or-the-egg, I can't say. *Lunar guitar* was an effort to make sense out of that first rhyme for *car*. I rather liked it; reminded me of a painting by Henri Rousseau, "The Sleeping Gypsy," which shows a figure with a stringed instrument lying in dreamy moonlight in the forest. But I didn't like it enough, because as you will notice, by the third sketch, it was gone. Here I was focusing on changing the strained image of *feather curled,* and I momentarily changed the original phrasing of the first line.

                                          edge   earth
#3   What will you find at the end of the world?
            a footprint,
            a feather,
              baby gull
            a fledgling curled   leaf uncurled
            a flag unfurled

             is that what there is at the edge of the world
             an arctic stone   cave
                           a tree of ice
                           an ocean cave,
        a lunar star   light from the stars-
                     signals
                          cluster of stars
                          exploding   expanding

                    message sealed in jars
                    or a broken bottle and a rusted car?
                         plastic container
                    a desert stretching far
                                             that
                    or do you find when you go so far
                    —or a junkyard of cars?

I didn't yet have an idea of precisely how many lines there would be,
but it was a one-stanza poem, I expected.

   The next sketch was primarily an attempt to widen the rhymes
from *car* and *world*.

                                        rim
                                       edge
#4   What will you find at the end of the world?
                                    horizon's end

         A footprint,
          a feather,
          a flag unfurled?   a cave of ice
          Is that what there is at the edge of the world?
    ghostly silence   a single·tree, the wind blowing free
                                             explored
                                             toward
              Or do you find when you go that far
                         a cluster   blaze   manmade stars
              a cavern reflecting light from the stars
              or a junkyard of cars?

I tried to pull things together and wrote out this:

#5A   What will you find at the edge of the world?
           A footprint,

                                                             61

a plastic container
and a rusted car?
a single pebble
bubble in sand   roar of the sea
a shell   sand bar-   a lunar landscape
metallic fin
a door left ajar   a leaf   a stone
a single flower in a field
buried gold   a prowling cat
a perfect bubble
creature unknown

In this version I was putting down whatever images came to mind that would convey isolation, the end of human civilization. Clichés were studded throughout the scribbled phrases, but I wasn't stopping to censor myself at this stage. (Incidentally, I later realized that A Single Pebble had been used as the title of a novel, and A Leaf, A Stone, A Door came from Thomas Wolfe.) *Buried gold, the roar of the sea, wind blowing free, ghostly silence:* these were almost perfect examples of the banal, but I went on anyway. The next sketch went back to the original: *What will you find at the edge of the world?* Now I felt on firm footing; no more changes in that opening: if I lost it, I'd lose the poem.

#5   A footprint,
a feather,
by the wind whorled   gnarled   snarled
a leaf uncurled,
a sea cave   engulfing darkness
snowfall
a feather,
a leaf uncurled,
a cave of ice,

a cluster of stars
or a junkyard of cars?

From that, a second stanza began to evolve and I felt a new rush of
excitement as the poem was taking shape. Bottles and containers
were out; the car image would be focused on doubly.

#5B   What will there be at the rim of the earth?

A perfect bubble,
a single tree,
a miracle birth?
the roar of the sea
the silence of planets stars
—or the traffic of cars?

When I read it over, the idea of traffic still moving and noise at
world's end struck me as wrong. So a variation emerged for the
second stanza.

#6   What will there be at the rim of the earth
                              outermost rim
                              horizon dim

lightning
thunder
   baby lamb's
a new creature's birth
horizons blazing   unending sunrise
              a sea cave deep   steep   sleep
              immortal sleep   creep
or cars piled up in a rusty heap.

The end now seemed right, and getting rid of the cliché of *miracle
birth* helped. I went back to work on what was now stanza one.

#7   What will you find at the edge of the world?
      A footprint,
      a feather,
       seedling curled lightning hurled
      a leaf uncurled
       single leaf curled
      engulfing darkness
      exploding stars
      a rainfall
         rainbow
         snowfall of stars

The final line of that stanza *or a junkyard of cars* was fixed, I felt, but the rhyme for *world* was still giving me trouble. I didn't like any of the images; they seemed stale (*lightning hurled*) or awkward (*seedling curled*). Curled in what? I could justify its use if I had to: the embryonic shape curled up into a ball, but rationalization was not going to complete the poem.

My next version, therefore, concentrated on trying to get a new *world* rhyme/image. I tried a white sheet of paper instead of lined yellow ledger sheets; maybe the snowy blankness would lead to fresh ideas? No luck. I even used a rhyming dictionary—something I rarely do. *Furled, twirled, swirled, whirled, skirled. Ocean waves whirled?* I realized by now this was an identical rhyme: so much for the dictionary's help! *Strange music skirled? A thunderbolt hurled? Desert sand swirled?* Discouraged, I went back to *a leaf uncurled* and put the poem aside.

A few days later I typed it out cleanly.

#7A   What will you find at the edge of the world?
      A footprint,
      a feather,
      a seedling curled?

Engulfing darkness,
a rainbow of stars,
or a junkyard of cars?

What will there be at the rim of the earth?
Lightning,
thunder,
a new creature's birth?
Unending sunrise,
immortal sleep,
or cars piled up in a rusty heap?

The fourth line was still a stopper to me. What if I substituted *thunderbolt hurled?* Then I'd have to take thunder out of the second stanza. And if I did, *engulfing darkness* and *a rainbow of stars* ought also to be dropped; they were too close in imagery to the thunderbolt.

So it now read:

#8   What will you find at the edge of the world?
        A footprint,
        a feather,
        a thunderbolt hurled?
        A tree of ice,
           snowfall   crown
        a garden
                    rain of stars,
        or a junkyard of cars?

        What will there be at the rim of the earth?
        A sand dune
        a crater,
        a new creature's birth?

Unending sunrise,
immortal sleep,
or cars piled up in a rusty heap?

The last three lines, like the first three, remained as they had been. *Rain of stars* was better than the three other choices, and I would settle for that. Still, *thunderbolt hurled* was no more satisfactory to me in the long run than *seedling curled*. At this point I became aware that if I continued to worry it, the poem would only deteriorate. Put it aside was self's advice to self.

Then, a month later, I was on a lecture trip in the Midwest. At night, in my hotel room, I thought over the poem again and wrote it down from memory. Immediately after I did, I crossed out the offending thunderbolt and wrote in *desert sand swirled,* elated that I had found a new image and completely unaware that it was one I had considered earlier. But using it brought the old problem of similar images. If there was desert sand in the first stanza, it would be impossible to have a sand dune in the second. How about instead of *sand dune* the word *canyon?* Or *sea cave?* Or *grass,* or *prairie? Coral reef?* A two-syllable phrase was needed to maintain the rhythm; *grass* and *coral reef* were eliminated. *Prairie* was not stripped bare enough for world's end. It would have to be *canyon.* Now the phrasing went:

a crater,
a canyon,
a new creature's birth.

Without even consciously saying to myself: too pat, too alliterative with all those hard c sounds, there suddenly jumped into my mind this sequence:

a mollusc,
a mammal,
a new creature's birth.

The sequence seemed right, and when I wrote it out it still seemed fitting. So here now is the poem. I'm still not altogether pleased; *desert sand swirled* is a little too sibilant to read aloud easily. Perhaps some day I'll find another image,* but for now I'm satisfied that the poem is what I want to say in the way I have found to say it.

* or perhaps you will

LANDSCAPE

What will you find at the edge of the world?
A footprint,
a feather,
desert sand swirled?
A tree of ice,
a rain of stars,
or a junkyard of cars?

What will there be at the rim of the earth?
A mollusc,
a mammal,
a new creature's birth?
Eternal sunrise,
immortal sleep,
or cars piled up in a rusty heap?

Eve Merriam believes that poetry for children should be fun but yet memorable and in a modern vein. Among her earlier books of poetry for children are: *Catch A Little Rhyme, There Is No Rhyme for Silver, It Doesn't Always Have to Rhyme,* and *Independent Voices.*

Miss Merriam writes not only poetry for children and young people, but also picture books for younger children and poetry and books for adults. Her first book of adult poetry *Family Circle* was awarded the Yale Series of Young Poets prize and was published with an introduction by Archibald MacLeish.

Miss Merriam has also conducted a weekly radio series on modern poetry for radio station WQXR in New York. She is a professional lecturer and makes her home in New York City with her husband and two sons.